5

Investigating God's World

Quizzes & Worksheets

A Beka Book® Pensacola, FL 32523-9100
an affiliate of PENSACOLA CHRISTIAN COLLEGE®

This book is designed for individual student purchase. The contents may not be reproduced. It is correlated with the text *Investigating God's World.* The Fifth Grade Science Curriculum contains daily lesson plans and other helps for teaching. A Scope and Sequence, answers to Comprehension Checks and Chapter Checkups found in the text, and other helpful information are contained in the Teacher Edition of *Investigating God's World.*

Investigating God's World Quizzes & Worksheets contains twenty-five quizzes and twenty-four worksheets that have been placed in the order in which they will be used.

The science quizzes are regularly scheduled throughout the semester. This schedule, as well as further testing and quizzing information, can be found in the Fifth Grade Science Curriculum.

Quiz answers and recommended grading scales are contained in the Teacher Key for this book. For all grading, subtract the total number of points missed from 100 points.

The science worksheets are included in this book to provide variety and vital practice. Worksheets should be checked but not graded. Answers are contained in the Teacher Key for this book.

Investigating God's World Tests, designed for individual student purchase, and a Teacher Key are also available.

Investigating God's World **Quizzes & Worksheets**
For use with fourth edition of text
Editorial Staff: A. Thayer, D. Mereness

Copyright © mmix, mcmxcix, mcmxci Pensacola Christian College
All rights reserved. Printed in U.S.A. 2011 C10

A Beka Book, a Christian textbook ministry affiliated with Pensacola Christian College, is designed to meet the need for Christian textbooks and teaching aids. The purpose of this publishing ministry is to help Christian schools reach children and young people for the Lord and train them in the Christian way of life.

Star illustrations on page 61, 65, 66 from *The Stars: A New Way to See Them* by H. A. Rey. Copyright © 1952, 1962, 1967, 1970, 1975, 1976 by H. A. Rey. Adapted and reprinted by permission of Houghton Mifflin Harcourt Publishing Company. All rights reserved.

Photo credits: Cover/title page—Stockbyte (diver); 7—Donald Specker/AnimalsAnimals (AA), Ken Cole/AA, James H. Robinson/AA, OSF/AA, Richard Shiell/AA, William E. Ferguson; 13—Tom McHugh/Taronga Zoo, Sydney/NAS/Photo Researchers, Inc. (PR), Stouffer Productions/AA, Hans Reinhard/Okapia/NAS/PR, Fritz Prenzel/AA, Mella Panzella/AA, Tom McHugh/NAS/PR; 27—Adobe and Corbis Images; 29, 31—Mountain High Maps (MHM) ® Copyright © 1997 Digital Vision, Inc.; 33—ABB, W. Ferguson (2), ABB, Lynn McLaren/PR, Breck P. Kent/Earth Scenes (ES); 67—Corbis Images; 71—Corbis Images, NASA/SS/PR, Corbis Images, NASA; 77—MHM; 79—Corbis Images, John Lemker/ES, Corbis, Eyewire, istockphoto.com/Glenn Culbertson, Eastcott/Momatiuk/ES, Joyce Photographics/SS/PR, W. Ferguson, Jim Steinberg/SS/PR; 87—Corel, Corbis Images, Adobe.

Name _____   Date _____   Score _____

QUIZ 1   *Investigating God's World*

Sections 1.3–1.4   –7 each

I. FILL IN THE BLANK: Write the answer that best completes the statement.

_____*goldenrod*_____   1. The __?__ plant may be the chief source of pollen and nectar for insects in the fall.

_____*pollination*_____   2. The transfer of pollen from the male parts to the female parts of plants is called __?__.

_____*pollen*_____   3. The "dust" that flowers use in producing seeds is called __?__.

_____*nectar*_____   4. Flowers use a sweet liquid called __?__ to attract insects.

_____*ovipositor*_____   5. The egg-laying "stinger" of a female insect is called its __?__.

II. MATCHING: Match the description with the bee.

__*D*__   6. male bee

__*B*__   7. female bee that mates and lays eggs

__*E*__   8. its nest is made of paper

__*C*__   9. will die a few hours after losing its stinger

A. bumblebee

B. queen

C. honeybee

D. drone

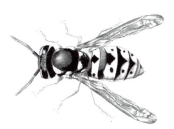

E. yellow jacket

Name _____   Date _____

Science Worksheet 1   *Investigating God's World*

Ch. 1

IDENTIFY: Label each insect.

1. _____*bumblebee*_____

2. _____*honeybee*_____

3. _____*yellow jacket*_____

4. _____*monarch butterfly*_____

5. _____*American hover fly*_____

6. _____*bee killer*_____

7. _____*drone fly*_____

8. _____*viceroy butterfly*_____

Name _____ Date _____ Score _____

QUIZ 2   *Investigating God's World*

Sections 1.5–1.6   *–8 each*

I. FILL IN THE BLANK: Write the answer that best completes the statement.

_____*camouflage*_____ 1. The ability of an animal to blend in with its background is called ? .

_____*piercing-sucking*_____ 2. True bugs have ? mouthparts.

_____*backbone*_____ 3. Invertebrates have no ? .

_____*green plant*_____ 4. Nearly every food chain begins with a ?   ? .

_____*mimicry*_____ 5. The American hover fly and the drone fly protect themselves by ? .

II. MATCHING: Match the term with the picture.

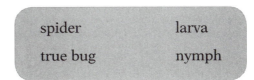

| spider | larva |
| true bug | nymph |

6. _____*nymph*_____   7. _____*true bug*_____

8. _____*larva*_____   9. _____*spider*_____

III. SHORT ANSWER: Answer the question in a complete sentence.

10. Why do gardeners want praying mantises in their gardens?

    Praying mantises eat harmful insects. _____

    _____

Name _____   Date _____

Science Worksheet 2   *Investigating God's World*

Ch. 1

I. IDENTIFY: Study the characteristics of these organisms, and write *true bug, beetle, fly, bee, butterfly,* or *spider* in the box.

1. _____*bee*_____

2. _____*butterfly*_____

3. _____*fly*_____

4. _____*spider*_____

5. _____*true bug*_____

6. _____*beetle*_____

★ Which of these are invertebrates? _____*all*_____

II. IDENTIFY each organism.

1. _____*praying mantis*_____

2. _____*ambush bug*_____

3. _____*aster*_____

4. _____*thistle*_____

5. _____*viceroy butterfly*_____

6. _____*goldenrod spider*_____

Name _____ Date _____ Score _____

I. FILL IN THE BLANK A: Write *beetle* or *true bug* in the blank.

_____beetle_____	1. I have chewing mouthparts.
_____true bug_____	2. I have piercing-sucking mouthparts.
_____beetle_____	3. I make up one fourth of all animals in the world.
_____true bug_____	4. My wings form a V or an X.

II. FILL IN THE BLANK B: Write the answer that best completes the statement.

_____composite_____	5. The flower family whose name means "made of many parts" is the _?_ family.
_____disk_____	6. The tiny yellow flowers in the center of the daisy are _?_ flowers.
_____ray_____	7. The white flowers that surround the center of the daisy are _?_ flowers.

III. WHO AM I? Write the answer in the blank.

_____nymph_____	8. I am a young mantis.
_____spider_____	9. Because I have only two body parts, I am not an insect.
_____goldenrod spider_____	10. I am the spider who turns white when I'm on the white part of the daisy and yellow when I'm on the yellow part.

QUIZ 4   *Investigating God's World*

Sections 2.1–2.3

FILL IN THE BLANK: Write the answer that best completes the statement. *–10 each*

backbones	1. Animals with _?_ are called "vertebrates."
habitat	2. Each mammal has its own _?_ where it likes to live.
four	3. Most mammals have _?_ limbs.
social	4. Animals that like to live in groups of the same kind are called _?_ animals.
marsupial	5. A kangaroo is a _?_ because its young finish developing in a special pouch.
mammary	6. Mammal mothers have _?_ glands to provide milk for their babies.
herbivores	7. Because all rodents eat plants, they are called _?_ .
rabbit	8. An animal that is **not** a rodent but is often mistaken for one is the _?_ .
nocturnal	9. An animal that is active at night is a _?_ animal.
echidna	10. The duckbill platypus and the _?_ are the only mammals which are not born alive; they hatch from eggs.

Name _____   Date _____

Science Worksheet 3   *Investigating God's World*
Ch. 2

I. CLASSIFY: Circle the name of each carnivore listed below.

(raccoon)   (bear)   (weasel)   (wolf)

echidna   (panda)   (tiger)   (skunk)

koala   pangolin   hedgehog   opossum

II. IDENTIFY: Put an *M* in the blank by each mammal that is a marsupial. Put an *E* in the blank by each mammal that is an egg-layer. If an animal is neither, leave the blank empty.

E 1. platypus

M 2. opossum   ____ 3. cat

M 4. kangaroo   *M* 5. koala   *E* 6. echidna

QUIZ 5   *Investigating God's World*

Sections 2.4–2.7

TRUE/FALSE: If the statement is true, write *true*. If the statement is false, replace the underlined word(s) with a word or phrase that will make the statement true. **Do not write *false* in any blank.** *–10 each*

bats	1. The only mammals that fly are <u>moles</u>.
insectivores	2. Mammals that eat insects are called <u>herbivores</u>.
true	3. Mammals that eat flesh (meat) are called <u>carnivores</u>.
true	4. When an animal's mother and father are of the same breed, that animal is a <u>purebred</u>.
packs	5. Wolves travel in <u>clans</u>.
instinct	6. An inherited behavior pattern in animals is called <u>intelligence</u>.
dogs	7. Scientists use the word *canines* to refer to all <u>cats</u>.
true	8. The only cat with a mane is the <u>lion</u>.
true	9. The fastest land animal on earth is the <u>cheetah</u>.
true	10. To insulate their bodies from icy Arctic waters, polar bears have a thick layer of <u>blubber</u>.

QUIZ 6   *Investigating God's World*

Sections 2.8–2.9   *–10 each*

I. MULTIPLE CHOICE: Write the letter of the correct answer in the blank.

_b_   1. Monkeys are different from apes because monkeys have _?_ .

         a. claws   **c.** fur
         b. tails   **d.** incisors

_d_   2. Older male gorillas with gray hairs on their backs are called _?_ .

         a. graybacks   **c.** silver gorillas
         b. old gray hairs   **d.** silverbacks

_a_   3. The padded cushion on the bottom of a horse's foot is called _?_ .

         a. a frog   **c.** the palm
         b. a toad   **d.** the heel

_c_   4. A newborn horse is called _?_ .

         a. a colt   **c.** a foal
         b. a filly   **d.** a mare

_b_   5. What animal has a donkey for a father and a horse for a mother?

         a. zebra   **c.** donkey
         b. mule   **d.** horse

II. MATCHING: Match the primate with its characteristic.

_D_   6. spider monkey

_A_   7. mountain gorilla

_E_   8. capuchin

_C_   9. chimpanzee

_B_   10. rhesus monkey

A. largest of all apes

B. Rh factor named after it

C. ape used as actor, astronaut, and for research

D. a New World monkey with a sensitive tail

E. a monkey trained to help paralyzed people

QUIZ 7   *Investigating God's World*

Sections 3.1–3.5   *–7 each*

I. FILL IN THE BLANK: Write the answer that best completes the statement.

energy _____   1. The ability to do work is called __?__ .

186,000 _____   2. Light travels at approximately __?__ miles per second.

transparent _____   3. An object that lets light pass through it completely is __?__ .

Thomas Edison _____   4. The inventor of the light bulb was __?__ __?__ .

reflection _____   5. The bouncing of light is __?__ .

refraction _____   6. The bending of light is __?__ .

II. SKETCH: Draw the lenses given below.

7. _____   8. _____

convex   concave

III. LISTING: List the colors of the spectrum in order.

Red _____

Orange _____

Yellow _____

Green _____

Blue _____

Violet _____

Science Worksheet 4   *Investigating God's World*

Ch. 3

I. COMPLETE: Show how light will travel by completing the drawings.

1. mirror

2. periscope

3. concave mirror

4. convex mirror

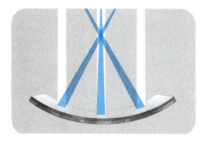

II. COLOR the diagram of the white light passing through a prism. Put the colors in the correct order.

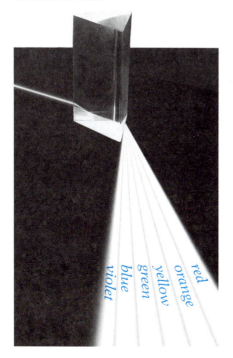

red
orange
yellow
green
blue
violet

Name _____   Date _____

Science Worksheet 5   *Investigating God's World*

Ch. 3

DIAGRAM: (1) Label the main parts of the eye with the following terms: *cornea, pupil,*
iris, lens, retina, optic nerve.
(2) With a green and a brown crayon, draw a picture of light coming from
the lamp into the eye.

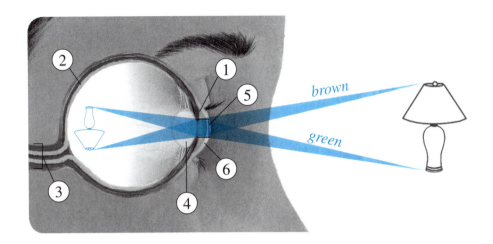

1. _____ *iris* _____

2. _____ *retina* _____

3. _____ *optic nerve* _____

4. _____ *lens* _____

5. _____ *pupil* _____

6. _____ *cornea* _____

QUIZ 8   *Investigating God's World*

Sections 3.6–3.7   *–10 each*

I. LABEL the parts of the eye.

1. _____*retina*_____
2. _____*iris*_____
3. _____*lens*_____
4. _____*pupil*_____
5. _____*cornea*_____

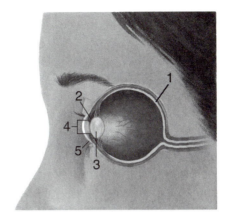

II. FILL IN THE BLANK: Write the answer that best completes the statement.

_____*tapetum*_____ 6. Some animals have an extra layer of cells called a __?__ that reflects like a mirror, allowing them to see in the dark.

_____*monocular*_____ 7. Animals whose eyes can move in two directions at once have __?__ vision.

_____*binocular*_____ 8. Because its eyes work together to produce an image of the same object, we say that a dog has __?__ vision.

_____*compound*_____ 9. Houseflies have __?__ eyes.

_____*irises*_____ 10. A person with blue eyes actually has blue __?__.

Science Worksheet 6

Investigating God's World

Ch. 3

I. CLASSIFY: Label each picture with **monocular vision** or **binocular vision.**

1. _monocular vision_   2. _monocular vision_   3. _binocular vision_

4. _monocular vision_   5. _binocular vision_

II. IDENTIFY: Below each insturment, name the scientist(s) who helped to develop it or used it to make a discovery.

1. _Sir Isaac Newton_   2. _Anton Van Leeuwenhoek_   3. _Thomas Edison_   4. _Hans Lippershey, Galileo, Sir Isaac Newton_

Name _____   Date _____

LABEL the layers of the earth and tell if the layer is solid, liquid, or both.

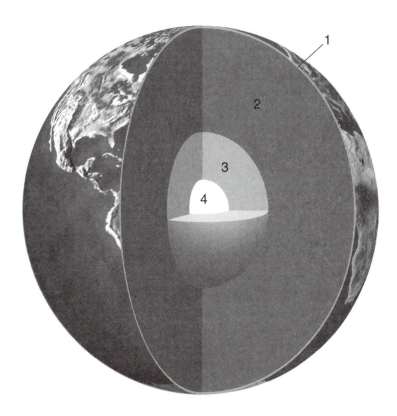

1. ____*crust, solid*____

2. ____*mantle, both*____

3. ___*outer core, liquid*___

4. ___*inner core, solid*___

QUIZ 9   *Investigating God's World*

Sections 4.1–4.3

I. LISTING A: Name the two types of weathering. *–10 each*

1. *chemical weathering*   2. *physical weathering*

II. LISTING B: (1) Name the three types of rocks. *–5 each*
(2) Give one example for each type. *(up to 30 total points)*

Type		*Example* *(Answers vary)*
3. *igneous*	6.	*obsidian, pumice, granite, basalt*
4. *sedimentary*	7.	*limestone sandstone, shale*
5. *metamorphic*	8.	*marble, slate*

III. IDENTIFY: Name the type of scientist who studies the earth. *–5 total*

9. *geologist*

IV. LABELING: Label the parts of the earth. *–10 each*

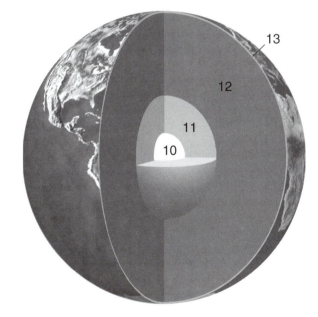

10. *inner core*

11. *outer core*

12. *mantle*

13. *crust*

Name _____   Date _____

Science Worksheet 8   *Investigating God's World*
Ch. 4

CLUES: Use the picture and the word clue to help you write the name of the rock and the type of rock.

1. volcanic glass

_____*obsidian*_____

_____*igneous*_____

2. made of sand

_____*sandstone*_____

_____*sedimentary*_____

3. changed from shale

_____*slate*_____

_____*metamorphic*_____

4. hardened lava foam

_____*pumice*_____

_____*igneous*_____

5. made from bones and seashells

_____*limestone*_____

_____*sedimentary*_____

6. changed from limestone

_____*marble*_____

_____*metamorphic*_____

7. smells like mud when it is wet

_____*shale*_____

_____*sedimentary*_____

8. contains minerals of different colors

_____*granite*_____

_____*igneous*_____

QUIZ 10   *Investigating God's World*

Sections 4.4–4.5   *–10 each*

I. MATCHING A: Match the mineral with its description.

_D_ 1. graphite   **A.** used in plaster of Paris

_A_ 2. gypsum   **B.** easily broken into flat sheets

_E_ 3. flint   **C.** "mud ball"

_B_ 4. mica   **D.** used in pencils

_C_ 5. geode   **E.** used for arrow heads

II. MATCHING B: Match the metal with its description.

_F_ 6. aluminum   **A.** best conductor of electricity

_C_ 7. mercury   **B.** most useful

_B_ 8. iron   **C.** liquid at room temperature

_A_ 9. silver   **D.** bright yellow

_E_ 10. uranium   **E.** source of nuclear power

                          F. lightweight, silvery colored, rustproof

Name _____ Date _____ Score _____

I. FILL IN THE BLANK: Write the answer that best completes the statement.

diamond   1. The hardest of all substances is the ? .

ruby   2. The rarest gemstone is the ? .

mineralogists   3. Scientists who study minerals are called ? .

coal   4. The brown or black rocklike substance used for fuel is called
                       ? .

petroleum   5. Oil in its natural state is called crude oil or ? .

fossils   6. The preserved remains of plants or animals are called ? .

spelunker   7. A person who explores caves is called a ? .

II. LABEL the cave formations.

column   stalactites   stalagmites

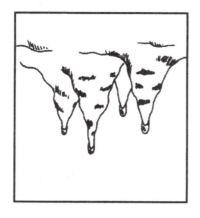

8. _____*stalactites*_____   9. _____*stalagmites*_____   10. _____*column*_____

Science Worksheet 9 *Investigating God's World*
Ch. 5

LABEL: Use the following terms to label the steps of the water cycle.

precipitation   evaporation   condensation

1. _____*evaporation*_____

2. _____*condensation*_____

3. _____*precipitation*_____

Science Worksheet 10

Ch. 5

Investigating God's World

I. LABEL the diagram, using the numbers on the list below.

1. barnacle

2. seaweed

3. mussel

4. sea anemone

5. crab

6. sea urchin

7. high intertidal zone

8. middle intertidal zone

9. low intertidal zone

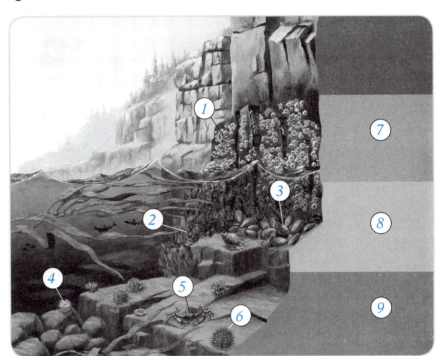

II. LABEL: Use the following terms to label the diagram.

blade   holdfast   air bladder

1. _____*blade*_____

2. _____*air bladder*_____

3. _____*holdfast*_____

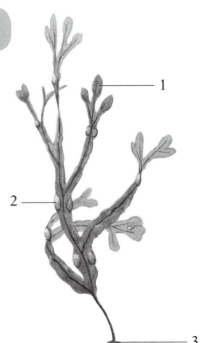

Name _____ Date _____ Score _____

I. LABEL the water cycle.

1. _____*condensation*_____

2. _____*precipitation*_____

3. _____*evaporation*_____

II. MULTIPLE CHOICE: Write the letter of the correct answer in the blank.

_____*c*_____ 4. Tiny floating plants and animals are called __?__.

    a. anemones   **c.** plankton
    b. sponges   **d.** polyps

_____*d*_____ 5. The scientific abbreviation for water is __?__.

    a. HO_2 **c.** O_2H
    b. H_3O **d.** H_2O

_____*b*_____ 6. The highest high tides and the lowest low tides are called __?__ tides.

    a. neap   **c.** low
    b. spring   **d.** high

_____*c*_____ 7. Seaweed is found in the __?__ zone.

    a. high tide   **c.** middle intertidal
    b. high intertidal   **d.** low intertidal

Name _____   Date _____

I. CLASSIFY: Label each picture *high, middle,* or *low* according to the intertidal zone in which the plant or animal lives.

1. _____ *low* _____   2. _____ *high* _____

3. _____ *middle* _____   4. _____ *middle* _____

II. LABEL the pictures **true seal** or **eared seal.** Explain what characteristics helped you to identify them.

1. _____ *true seal* _____   2. _____ *eared seal* _____

_____ *no outer ears* _____   _____ *small outer ears* _____

_____ *small flippers that are of* _____   _____ *flippers that enable the seal* _____

_____ *no use to the seal on land* _____   _____ *to sit up and walk on land* _____

Name _____   Date _____   Score _____

I. MATCHING: Match the sea creature with its description.

_D_ 1. shrimp

_E_ 2. starfish

_A_ 3. conch

_C_ 4. oyster

_B_ 5. sea anemone

A. a univalve

B. looks like a flower

C. pearls form inside

D. small crustacean

E. has tube feet

F. a carnivorous snail

II. FILL IN THE BLANK: Write the answer that best completes the statement.

___stonefish___   6. I am the most poisonous fish.

___parrotfish___   7. I am a fish that has fused teeth.

___wrasse___   8. I am a fish that cleans the bodies of larger fish without hurting them.

___sea horse___   9. I have a pouch to carry the eggs my mate lays.

III. SHORT ANSWER: Answer the question in a complete sentence.

10. What is a pinniped?

  Pinnipeds are "wing-footed" mammals such as walruses, seals, and sea lions.

QUIZ 14   *Investigating God's World*

Sections 5.4–5.8

TRUE/FALSE: If the statement is true, write *true*. If the statement is false, replace the underlined word(s) with a word or phrase that will make the statement true. **Do not write *false* in any blank.** *−10 each*

wandering albatross	1. The largest of all flying birds is the <u>penguin</u>.
true	2. Penguins live in colonies called <u>rookeries</u>.
warm-blooded	3. Birds are <u>cold-blooded</u> creatures.
true	4. Scientists who study the sea are called <u>oceanographers</u>.
true	5. The layer of fat that keeps animals warm is <u>blubber</u>.
true	6. One of the few animals that successfully preys on sea urchins is the <u>sea otter</u>.
eared	7. The seals that have small ears are <u>true</u> seals.
porcupine fish	8. The fish that puffs itself up and makes its spines stick out when it feels threatened is the <u>blenny</u>.
true	9. Coral reefs are formed by <u>coral polyps</u>.
crustaceans	10. Because they have a crustlike shell, lobsters are classififed as <u>mollusks</u>.

Name _____   Date _____   Score _____

Sections 6.1–6.3   *–10 each*

I. MULTIPLE CHOICE: Write the letter of the correct answer in the blank.

___d___   1. The term _?_ can be defined as "a push or pull."
  a. gravity   **c.** mass
  b. friction   **d.** force

___c___   2. What kind of force occurs when one object pushes against another?
  a. gravity   **c.** contact force
  b. friction   **d.** motion

___b___   3. A force that resists motion is called _?_.
  a. contact force   **c.** gravity
  b. friction   **d.** mass

___a___   4. The force of attraction between objects is known as _?_.
  a. gravity   **c.** contact force
  b. motion   **d.** friction

___c___   5. What kind of force do you use when you tap your pencil?
  a. gravity   **c.** contact force
  b. friction   **d.** mass

II. FILL IN THE BLANK: Tell whether each example represents *potential* or *kinetic* energy.

_____kinetic_____   6. a boy opening a can of soda

____potential____   7. an unopened can of soda

_____kinetic_____   8. a girl jumping rope

____potential____   9. a book on the edge of a table

____potential____   10. a parked car

Name _____ Date _____ Score _____

Sections 6.4–6.6   *–10 each*

I. LISTING: Name the invention man uses to harness the power of water.

1. _____*water wheel*_____

II. FILL IN THE BLANK: Write the correct answer in the blank.

_____*solid*_____   2. the state of matter that has a definite shape

_____*liquid*_____   3. the state of matter that has no definite shape, but its molecules tend to stay together

_____*gas*_____   4. the state of matter that has no definite shape, and its molecules tend to diffuse

_____*32°F*_____   5. the freezing point and melting point of water

_____*212°F*_____   6. the boiling point and condensation point of water

III. LABEL the parts of the steam engine.

7. _____*wheel*_____

8. _____*connecting rod*_____

9. _____*piston*_____

10. _____*cylinder*_____

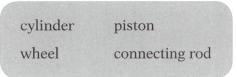

cylinder   piston

wheel   connecting rod

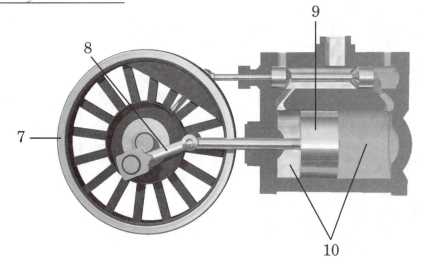

Name _____ Date _____

PUZZLE: Use the clues below to fill in the crossword puzzle.

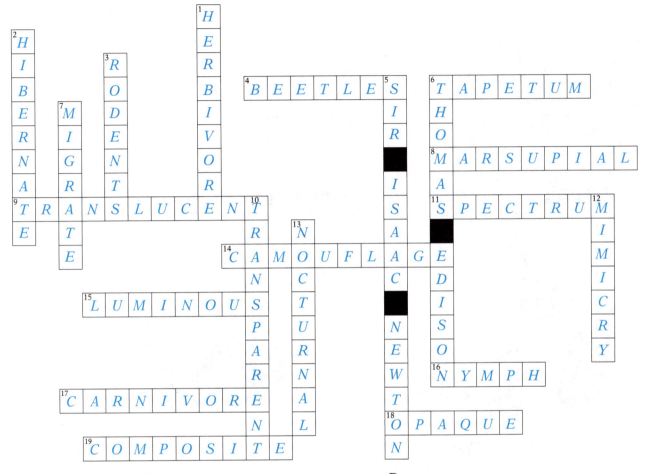

Across

4. the largest group of insects
6. the layer of cells many nocturnal animals have behind the retina
8. a mammal whose baby finishes developing in a pouch
9. an object that allows light to pass through, but which cannot be seen through
11. the series of colored bands created when sunlight is separated
14. to blend in with the surroundings
15. an object that produces its own light
16. an immature insect that looks like the adult
17. an animal that eats mostly meat
18. an object that does not let light pass through it
19. the largest family of flowering plants

Down

1. a plant-eating animal
2. to spend the winter in sleep
3. the largest group of mammals
5. inventor of the reflecting telescope
6. inventor of the lightbulb
7. to move from place to place with the changing seasons
10. an object that allows light to pass straight through
12. to look like another animal for protection
13. an animal that is active at night

Name _____   Date _____

Science Worksheet 12B   *Investigating God's World*

Ch. 6

I. APPLY: Check the actions below that cause work to be done.

___✓___ throwing a baseball   ___✓___ raking leaves

_____ lying still on a bed   _____ pushing against a locked door

___✓___ lifting a heavy box   ___✓___ pulling a wagon

___✓___ lifting a feather   ___✓___ pedaling a bicycle

_____ leaning up against a large tree

II. LABEL: Tell if the picture illustrates **kinetic energy** or **potential energy.** Write your answer in the space provided.

1. _____*potential energy*_____   2._____*kinetic energy*_____

III. APPLY: Tell what would need to be done for potential energy to be changed to kinetic energy.

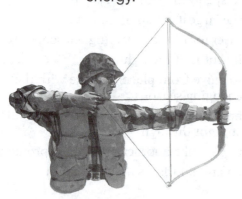

2. _____*let go of the balloon*_____

1. _____*release the bowstring*_____

3. _____*spring the trap*_____   4. _____*bump the table*_____

56

QUIZ 17   *Investigating God's World*

Sections 6.2–6.8   *–10 each*

FILL IN THE BLANK: Write the answer that best completes the statement.

repel _____   1. Like charges _?_; opposite charges attract.

lodestones _____   2. Early compasses were made from rocks called _?_.

transfer _____   3. When one object gives some or all of its energy to another object, _?_ of energy takes place.

melting _____   4. The temperature at which a solid becomes a liquid is called the _?_ point.

boiling _____   5. The temperature at which liquid becomes a gas is called the _?_ point.

freezing _____   6. The temperature at which a liquid becomes a solid is called the _?_ point.

burning _____   7. Combustion is another word for _?_.

oxygen _____   8. All fuels need _?_ in order to burn.

octane _____   9. The higher the _?_ number of a gasoline, the better the "anti-knock" quality.

propeller (prop) _____   10. The engine of the first airplane turned a _?_ that pulled the airplane through the air.

Name _____   Date _____

Science Worksheet 13A   *Investigating God's World*

Ch. 4–5 Review

PUZZLE: Write the answer to each clue; then write the circled letters in the blanks below to uncover a hidden message.

1. The mineral used as pencil "lead"   (G) R A P H I T E
                                              1

2. The most useful metal   I R (O) N
                                   2

3. A rocklike "mudball" full of crystals   G E O (D) E
                                                  3

4. A common sedimentary rock   L I M E (S) T O N E
                                          4

5. Only metal liquid at room temperature   (M) E R C U R Y
                                                  5

6. A mollusk with two hinged shells   B I V (A) L V E
                                                6

7. A metal that provides nuclear power   U (R) A N I U M
                                                7

8. A mollusk with a single shell   U N I (V) A L V E
                                              8

9. A "wing-footed" mammal   P I N N I P (E) D
                                            9

10. Coral reefs are formed by these   C O R A (L) P O L Y P S
                                                10

11. The most poisonous fish   S T (O) N E F I S H
                                    11

12. An igneous rock that floats   P (U) M I C E
                                        12

13. The best conductor of electricity   (S) I L V E R
                                              13

14. Largest flying bird   (W) A N D E R I N G A L B A T R O S S
                               14

15. Fish that looks like a snake   M (O) R A Y E E L
                                         15

16. Rarest gem   (R) U B Y
                      16

17. Carnivorous sea snail   W H E L (K)
                                      17

18. Sea invertebrates with crusty shells   C R U (S) T A C E A N S
                                                  18

Science is the study of G O D ' S   M A R V E L O U S   W O R K S .
                         1 2 3 4   5 6 7 8 9 10 11 12 13   14 15 16 17 18

Name _____   Date _____

Science Worksheet 13B   *Investigating God's World*

Ch. 6

I. IDENTIFY: Label the parts of the steam engine by filling in the numbered blanks below.

1. _____*cylinder*_____

2. _____*piston*_____

3. _____*connecting rod*_____

4. _____*wheel*_____

5. _____*piston rod*_____

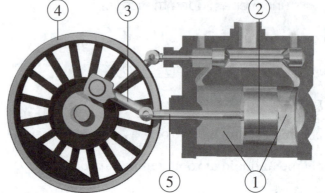

II. LABEL the parts of the steam locomotive by filling in the numbered blanks below.

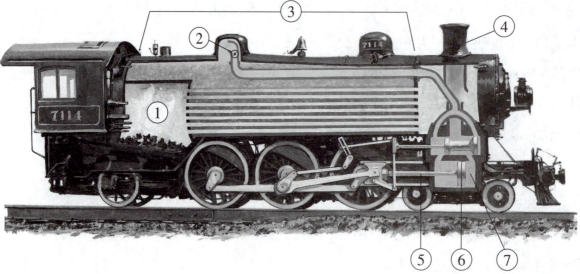

1. ___*furnace (firebox)*___   5. _____*piston rod*_____

2. _____*throttle*_____   6. _____*piston*_____

3. _____*boiler*_____   7. _____*cylinder*_____

4. _____*smokestack*_____

QUIZ 18 _____ *Investigating God's World*

Sections 7.1–7.2 _____ *–10 each*

I. FILL IN THE BLANK: Write the answer that best completes the statement.

sun spots	1. The dark spots on the surface of the sun are called _?_ _?_ .
93,000,000	2. The sun is _?_ miles from earth.
photosphere	3. The part of the sun that we see is called the _?_ .
core	4. The very center of the sun is called the _?_ .
corona	5. The vapor blanket around the sun is the _?_ .
god	6. Many ancient people thought the sun was a _?_ .
photosynthesis	7. The sun helps plants produce food through the process of _?_ .

II. LABEL the constellation.

8. *Big Dog (Canis Major)*   10. *Scorpion or Scorpius*

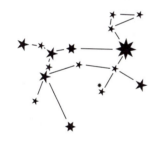

9. *Southern Cross*

Science Worksheet 14   *Investigating God's World*

Ch. 7

LABEL the layers of the sun. Tell which layer has a sunspot by placing a star beside the
correct label.

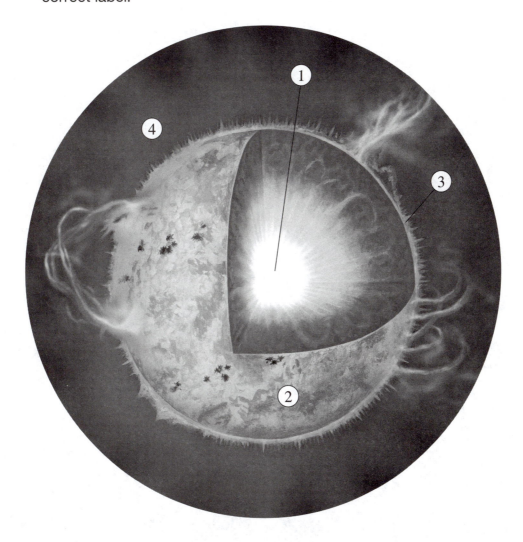

1. _____ *core* _____

2. _____ *photosphere* ★ _____

3. _____ *chromosphere* _____

4. _____ *corona* _____

Science Worksheet 15   *Investigating God's World*
Ch. 7

COMPLETE: Connect the stars to show the constellations. Label the constellations and
the important stars.

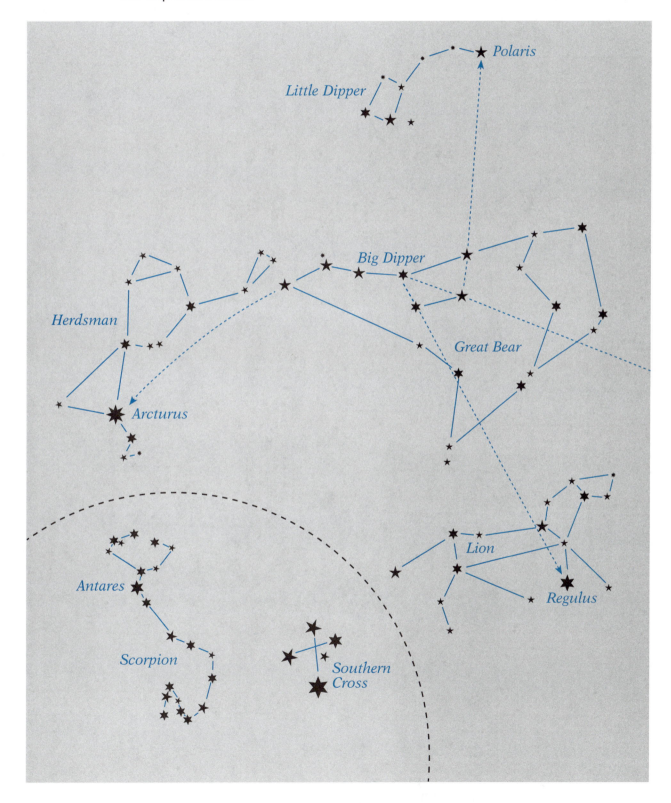

COMPLETE (cont.)

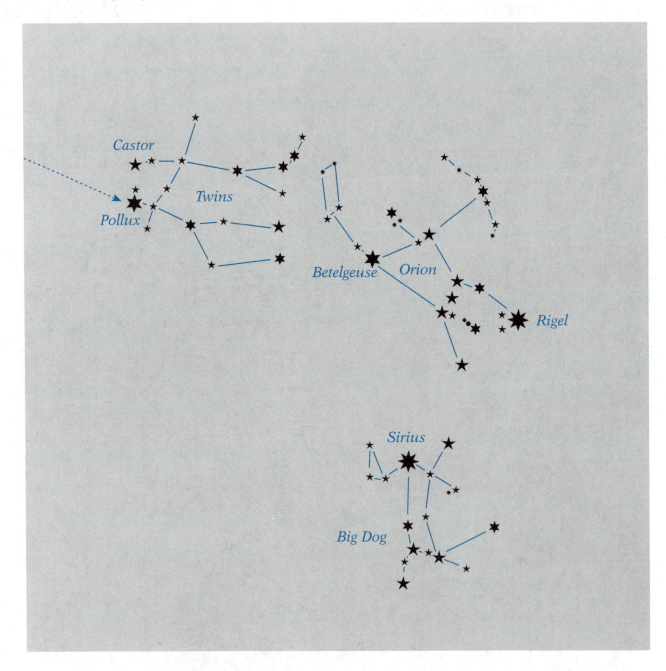

Name _____ Date _____ Score _____

QUIZ 19   *Investigating God's World*

Sections 7.3–7.4   *–6 each*

I. LABEL the phase of the moon.

1. _____*New Moon*_____

2. _____*Crescent*_____

3. _____*First Quarter*_____

4. _____*Gibbous*_____

5. _____*Full Moon*_____

6. _____*Gibbous*_____

7. _____*Third Quarter*_____

8. _____*Crescent*_____

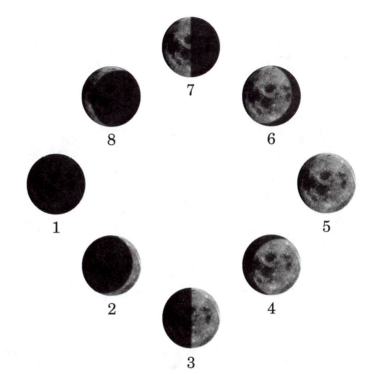

II. WHOM AM I? Identify the planets described and write the answer in the blank.

_____*Saturn*_____ 9. I have seven rings.

_____*Mars*_____ 10. I am the "red planet."

_____*Neptune*_____ 11. I have a royal blue atmosphere with very strong winds.

_____*Mercury*_____ 12. I am the closest planet to the sun.

_____*Earth*_____ 13. I am the only planet in the solar system suitable for life.

_____*Venus*_____ 14. I am the brightest planet.

_____*Uranus*_____ 15. I am tipped over to one side.

_____*Jupiter*_____ 16. I am the largest planet.

QUIZ 20   *Investigating God's World*

Sections 7.5–7.6   *–10 each*

TRUE/FALSE: If the statement is true, write *true.* If the statement is false, replace the
underlined word(s) with a word or phrase that will make the statement true.
Do not write *false* in any blank.

true	1. When air is cooled, it <u>contracts</u>, and takes up less space.
nitrogen	2. Air is mostly made up of <u>oxygen</u> (78%).
true	3. The total weight of air on a particular object is <u>air pressure</u>.
troposphere	4. The layer of the atmosphere closest to earth is the <u>stratosphere</u>.
true	5. The layer where weather occurs is the <u>troposphere</u>.
true	6. The invisible shield of gas that protects the earth is the <u>ozone</u> layer.
meteoroids	7. Pieces of space debris that hurtle through our atmosphere are called <u>mesospheres</u>.
true	8. Atoms that have lost electrons are called <u>ions</u>.
true	9. Another name for the northern lights is <u>aurora borealis</u>.
North Pole	10. The north magnetic pole is located near the geographic <u>South Pole</u>.

Name _____   Date _____

Science Worksheet 16   *Investigating God's World*

Ch. 7

I. IDENTIFY: Which phase of the moon is shown in each picture?

1. _____*gibbous*_____   2. _____*crescent*_____   3. _____*full moon*_____

4. ____*(third) quarter*____   5. _____*new moon*_____

II. LABEL each planet.

1. _____*Mercury*_____   4. _____*Mars*_____   7. _____*Uranus*_____

2. _____*Venus*_____   5. _____*Jupiter*_____   8. _____*Neptune*_____

3. _____*Earth*_____   6. _____*Saturn*_____

Science Worksheet 17 *Investigating God's World*
Ch. 7

LABEL the layers of the atmosphere.

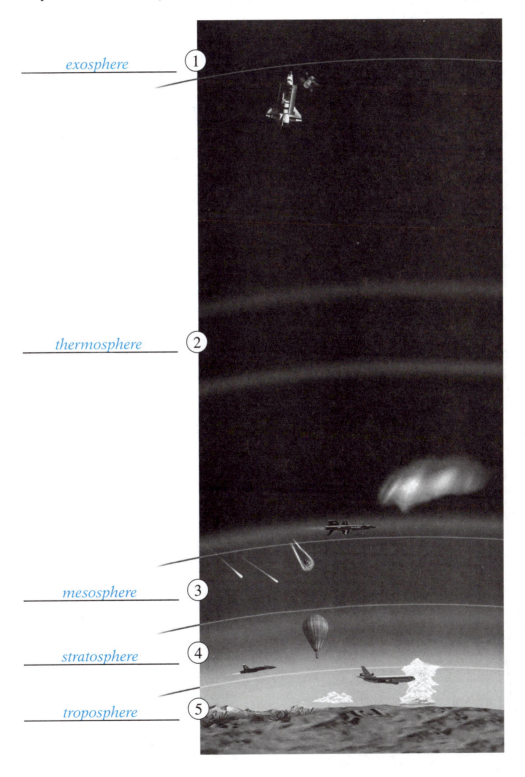

exosphere   ①

thermosphere   ②

mesosphere   ③

stratosphere   ④

troposphere   ⑤

Name _____ Date _____ Score _____

I. FILL IN THE BLANK: Write the answer that best completes the statement.

meteorologists   1. Scientists who study the weather are called _?_.

sun   2. The basic cause of all weather is the _?_.

greenhouse   3. The natural function in which the atmosphere keeps heat from escaping from the earth is called the _?_ effect.

equator   4. The imaginary line encircling the earth halfway between the North and South Poles is the _?_.

Hemisphere   5. The southern half of the earth is called the Southern _?_.

warm/hot   6. Air rises when it is _?_.

1,000   7. The earth spins at over _?_ miles per hour.

II. LIST the three major wind systems.

8. _*trade winds*_

9. _*polar easterlies*_

10. _*prevailing westerlies*_

Science Worksheet 18   *Investigating God's World*
Ch. 8

LABEL: Use the terms listed below to label the wind systems on the diagram of the earth. Each answer will be used twice.

> polar easterlies   trade winds   prevailing westerlies

1. _____*polar easterlies*_____

2. _*prevailing westerlies*_

3. *(northeast) trade winds*

4. *(southeast) trade winds*

5. _*prevailing westerlies*_

6. _____*polar easterlies*_____

Science Worksheet 19   *Investigating God's World*
Ch. 8

LABEL each cloud.

cumulonimbus
_____

stratus
_____

altocumulus
_____

cumulus
_____

stratocumulus
_____

cirrocumulus
_____

cirrostratus
_____

cirrus
_____

fog
_____

QUIZ 22   *Investigating God's World*

Sections 8.3–8.6   *–8 each*

I. **LIST** the three ingredients for clouds.

1. _____ *water* _____

2. _____ *rising air* _____

3. _____ *dust* _____

II. **WHAT KIND OF CLOUD AM I?** Write the answer in the blank.

_____ *cumulus* _____   4. I am a puffy cloud that is seen during good weather.

_____ *stratus* _____   5. I am a low blanket of cloud that indicates rain is coming.

_____ *cirrus* _____   6. I am a wispy cloud high in the sky.

_____ *fog* _____   7. I am the only cloud on ground level.

III. **MATCHING:** Match the type of precipitation with its description.

_E_	8. rain	**A.** ice crystals that stick together
_A_	9. wet snow	**B.** ice crystals that fall to the earth singly
_B_	10. dry snow	**C.** ice crystals that melt and refreeze in the air
_C_	11. sleet	**D.** ice crystals that form pieces of ice in thunderheads and are tossed around in the cloud until too heavy
_D_	12. hail	**E.** ice crystals that melt and fall to earth in liquid form

Name _____   Date _____

DIAGRAM: In each blank, write the term that corresponds with that number in the diagram of the cumulonimbus cloud.

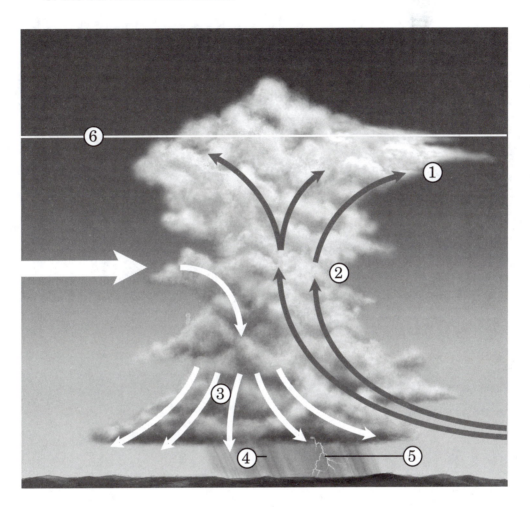

1. _____*anvil top*_____

2. _____*updrafts*_____

3. _____*downdrafts*_____

4. _____*rain*_____

5. _____*lightning*_____

6. _____*tropopause*_____

QUIZ 23   *Investigating God's World*

Sections 9.1–9.2

I. LISTING: (1) List the five classes of vertebrates.
(2) Indicate whether they are warm-blooded or cold-blooded.
–5 each (up to 50 total points)

	Class		*Warm-blooded or Cold-blooded*
1.	*mammals*	6.	*warm-blooded*
2.	*birds*	7.	*warm-blooded*
3.	*fish*	8.	*cold-blooded*
4.	*reptiles*	9.	*cold-blooded*
5.	*amphibians*	10.	*cold-blooded*

II. FILL IN THE BLANK: Write the correct bird for the description. *–10 each*

ostrich	11.	largest bird
birds of paradise	12.	birds from New Guinea whose beauty few other birds can match
hornbills	13.	birds that wall themselves up in nests
hummingbird	14.	only bird that hovers
peregrine falcon	15.	bird that has an air diving speed of 220 miles per hour or more

Name _____   Date _____

Science Worksheet 21   *Investigating God's World*

Ch. 9

CLASSIFY: Study the characteristics of these vertebrates and write **mammal, bird, reptile, fish,** or **amphibian** in the numbered space under the picture. Also write **cold** if the animal is cold-blooded, or **warm** if it is warm-blooded.

1. _____*amphibian*_____

   _____*cold*_____

2. _____*bird*_____

   _____*warm*_____

3. _____*fish*_____

   _____*cold*_____

4. _____*mammal*_____

   _____*warm*_____

5. _____*reptile*_____

   _____*cold*_____

6. _____*mammal*_____

   _____*warm*_____

7. _____*reptile*_____

   _____*cold*_____

8. _____*fish*_____

   _____*cold*_____

QUIZ 24   *Investigating God's World*

Sections 9.3–9.5   *–10 each*

I. LIST the three groups of fish.

1. _____*jawless fish*_____

2. ___*cartilaginous fish*___

3. _____*bony fish*_____

II. MATCHING: Match the snake with its description.

D	4. blind snake	**A.** perhaps the deadliest
C	5. python	**B.** bites more people than any other poisonous snake in America
A	6. taipan	**C.** squeezes prey
E	7. cobra	**D.** smallest snake
B	8. copperhead	**E.** largest poisonous snake

III. SHORT ANSWER: Answer the question in a complete sentence.

9. How can you tell the poisonous coral snake from the nonpoisonous scarlet king snake?

   Remember the difference between a coral snake and a scarlet king snake by memorizing

   this rhyme: red on yellow, kill a fellow; red on black, venom lack.

   _____

10. What is molting? *Molting is the process of shedding the outer layer of skin.*

   _____

   _____

Science Worksheet 22   *Investigating God's World*

Ch. 9

CLASSIFY: Label each picture **bony, jawless,** or **cartilaginous,** according to the type of
fish it is.

1.   white shark

_____*cartilaginous*_____

2.   flounder

_____*bony*_____

3.   stingray

_____*cartilaginous*_____

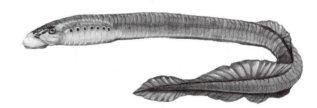

4.   lamprey

_____*jawless*_____

5.   goldfish

_____*bony*_____

6.   trout

_____*bony*_____

7.   hagfish

_____*jawless*_____

Name _____ Date _____ Score _____

QUIZ 25   *Investigating God's World*

Sections 9.6–9.8   *–10 each*

TRUE/FALSE: If the statement is true, write *true*. If the statement is false, replace the
    underlined word(s) with a word or phrase that will make the statement true.
    Do not write *false* in any blank.

_____*horned lizard*_____ 1. The lizard that can squirt a stream of blood at its enemies is
                              the <u>chuckwalla</u>.

_____*true*_____ 2. The largest lizard is the <u>Komodo dragon</u>.

_____*gila monster*_____ 3. The only poisonous lizards in the world are the Mexican
                              beaded lizard and the <u>chameleon</u>.

_____*carapace*_____ 4. The rounded upper section of a turtle's shell is its <u>scutes</u>.

_____*true*_____ 5. Tortoises are <u>land turtles</u>.

_____*alligators*_____ 6. The crocodilians normally found in the southeastern United
                              States and in China are <u>crocodiles</u>.

_____*true*_____ 7. The crocodilians that have some bottom teeth that stick out all
                              the time are the <u>crocodiles</u>.

_____*frogs*_____ 8. The amphibian known for its long hind legs and slimy skin is
                              the <u>toad</u>.

_____*true*_____ 9. Baby frogs and toads are called <u>tadpoles</u>.

_____*true*_____ 10. The amphibian that has suction pads on its toes is the <u>tree
                              frog</u>.

Science Worksheet 23   *Investigating God's World*

Ch. 9

IDENTIFY: Label the following reptiles. Explain what characteristics helped you to identify
them.

Sea turtle or tortoise?

1. _____*sea turtle*_____   2. _____*tortoise*_____

   ___*lives in the ocean; has*___   ___*lives on land; has legs*___

   ___*flippers instead of legs*___   ___*instead of flippers*___

Crocodile or alligator?

3. _____*alligator*_____   4. _____*crocodile*_____

   ___*broad head; no bottom*___   ___*thin head; top and*___

   ___*teeth sticking out*___   ___*bottom teeth sticking out*___

Caiman or gavial?

5. _____*caiman*_____   6. _____*gavial*_____

   ___*short, broad mouth*___   ___*long, narrow mouth;*___

   _____   ___*hundreds of teeth*___

Science Worksheet 24 _____ *Investigating God's World*
Ch. 9

ORDER: Number in order the steps of metamorphosis of a tadpole.

3   1   4

5   2